Stuck Inside

Activity Book

By Angie Woodworth

Illustrated by Lee Anderson

Anchor Book Press • Palatine

Stuck Inside Activity Book
Copyright ©2020 by Angie Woodworth
Illustrations Copyright ©2020 Lee Anderson
Cover Ink by Cirith Anderson
ISBN: 9781949109429
Printed in the United States
Anchor Book Press, Ltd
440 W. Colfax Street, Unit 1132
Palatine, IL 60078

Dear Parents,

We are living in scary times. Many adults are facing increased fear and anxiety. Our children are not immune to these same feelings. It is important to talk about things that are upsetting to children, but it is often difficult to bring up topics. *Stuck Inside* is written so that children can see that others are facing the same situation. In addition, topics are brought up that your children might want to talk about. Many times, children feel safer talking about a character like Ben than about what is happening in their family. This book is also appropriate to start discussions for other issues children are facing, such as a serious illness.

This book is a blackline master. You may copy the activity pages for your children as often as you would like. Note: Some activities require adult supervision, depending on the age of your child or children. Please discuss with child, in advance, that some activities need adult help or adult set up. Other activities do not require an adult, but they should ask permission first and be willing to clean up any mess.

My mom woke me up and said, "Ben, no school today."

I looked out my window and thought, "Why? It's not a snow day."

I got out of bed and everyone was home.

I didn't really understand what was going on.

No work for my parents. Is this a vacation?

Then while eating breakfast, the news said there is something wrong with the nation.

I'm just a kid so I don't really understand.

Why is everyone looking so worried and sad?

My mom tried to explain it the best that she could.

People are sick in some neighborhoods.

The TV man said to stay inside. These are the rules, so we have to abide.

I can't go see grandma or my friends. I can't even go
out eat. I feel so locked up, I want to cry and stomp
my feet.

People are acting crazy at the grocery store. They are buying everything so others can't get anymore.

All the toilet paper, and water too. What's a kid to use when he has to go poo?

My parents are whispering and hugging each other.

I'm sitting here not even fighting, quietly watching TV with my brother.

Things seem peaceful today and I feel like everything will be okay.

Just wash your hands, stay inside, and don't forget to pray.

Journal Page

Copy one page for each week. Make a book about the time school was closed.

(Tell one thing you learned this week)

_____

_____

(Write about the funniest thing that happened this week.)

_____

_____

_____

_____

(Write about the best thing that happened this week.)

_____

_____

_____

_____

Categories

To Play: Each person writes as many words as they can.

Optional: Timer set for 1 minute.

Copy this sheet and cut the game sheets apart.

Category: Food — Write words that start with the letter B.

Name: _____	Name: _____	Name: _____	Name: _____
_____	_____	_____	_____
_____	_____	_____	_____
_____	_____	_____	_____
_____	_____	_____	_____
_____	_____	_____	_____
_____	_____	_____	_____
_____	_____	_____	_____

Categories

To Play: Each person writes as many words as they can.

Optional: Timer set for 1 minute.

Copy this sheet and cut the game sheets apart.

Fill in new category and letter

Write words that start with the letter _____.

Category: _____

Name: _____

Name: _____

Name: _____

Name: _____

21

Activity Cards

(Copy and then cut apart)

Hot Potato

Roll up a pair of socks. Everyone sits in a circle. Set a timer for 15 seconds. Pass the sock to the person next to you. Don't be stuck with the sock when the timer goes off.

Book

Write your own book about being stuck inside. You decide if it is a true story or fiction. Fold sheets of paper in half to make the book. Staple along the edge.

Dream Car

Draw a dream car that can do anything – fly, sail, or whatever you can imagine.

Talent Show

Have a family talent show – sing, dance, draw.

Game Night

Play cards or a board game with your family.

Imaginary Vehicle

Use an old box or storage crate to create a vehicle. Use several to make a train.

Activity Cards

(Copy and then cut apart)

Go for a Walk

Find things that start with the first letter of your name.

Dance Party

Have a dance party with your family in your pajamas.

Nature Hunt

Looks for animals, flowers, trees, bugs, and rocks. What is the most unusual thing you saw?

Family Game

Have a taste test while wearing a blindfold.

Phone Call

Call a family member. Ask how they are doing. Tell them something funny that happened or something new you learned and tell them you love them.

Telephone

Sit in a circle. The first person whispers a secret to the next person. Go around the circle to see how much the secret changes from the first person to the last person.

Activity Cards

(Copy and then cut apart)

Airplane Race

Goal: Make an airplane go farther by changing the design.

1. Make a paper airplane.
2. Throw it – measure or mark the distance.
3. Make a new airplane (look on internet for ideas).
4. Throw it – did it go farther?

Bubbles

Ask permission. Make bubbles by mixing 3 cups water with 1/3 cup sugar. Stir till sugar is totally mixed in. Add 1/3 cup dish soap. Stir gently.

Put in unbreakable jars or containers.

Make a wand using a popsicle stick and pipe cleaners. Or use other things you have at home. A wand from an empty jar of bubbles can be used if you have one.

Sidewalk Chalk

Draw pictures or write messages on the sidewalk with colored chalk.

Activity Cards

(Copy and then cut apart)

Hide Out

Make a tent with pillows and blankets (ask permission). Hang a blanket over 2 or 3 chairs. Put pillows under blanket for seating. Use the tent to take a nap, read a book, draw a picture, or any fun activity. Use a flashlight or leave a corner open for light.

Picnic

Spread a blanket on the floor. Have lunch on the blanket. Use the baby's sippy cup or mom or dad's travel mug for juice or milk (ask first) so you don't spill anything on the floor.

Clean up everything when you are finished.

Make Cards

Make cards for relatives you cannot visit or people in the nursing home (it is ok if you don't know them - they will love the card anyway). Draw a pretty picture on the front. Write a nice note or just "Have a Nice Day" on the inside.

Ask your mom or dad to mail the cards.

Science Experiments

Work with an adult.

Make Play Dough

Supplies:

½ cup salt
1 T cream of tartar
1 cup warm water
1 T vegetable oil
Food coloring (optional)
1 cup flour

1. Mix salt, cream of tartar, warm water, and oil.
2. Add flour and mix.
3. Add a couple drops of food coloring.
4. Store in Ziploc Freezer bags.

(If you do not have cream of tartar, you can still make the play dough, but it will not last as long.

Clean Pennies

Supplies:

Pennies
Baking Soda
Vinegar

1. Put pennies in a shallow dish or container.
2. Sprinkle with baking soda.
3. Cover with vinegar.
4. Let sit for 20 minutes.
5. Take pennies out and dry.

Will this activity clean other coins?

Make Oobleck

Supplies:
2 cups corn starch
1 cup water
Food coloring

1. Mix corn starch and water.
2. Add food coloring, if desired.

Store in Ziploc Freezer bag.

Science Experiments

Work with an adult.

Make a Volcano

Supplies:

1 empty 2-liter pop bottle
2 t baking soda
¼ c vinegar
5 t dishwashing detergent
9 x 13 pan

1. Put pop bottle in pan.
2. Put 2 cups of warm water in bottle.
3. Add soap and baking soda.
4. Add vinegar.

(Wrap towel around pan to catch any overflow.)
For a more elaborate project, create a mountain landscape with Play-doh and twigs around bottle.

Create Gumdrop Structure

Supplies:

10 gumdrops
20 toothpicks
Paper towels

1. Use paper towel to work on.
2. Create structure using gumdrops and toothpicks.

1 set of supplies for each child or team.

Make Giant Bubbles

Supplies:
6 cups water
2/3 cup sugar
2/3 cup dish soap
Dishpan or another container

1. Mix water and sugar until sugar dissolves.
2. Gently stir in dish soap.
3. Pour into container.
4. Make bubble wand with wire clothes hanger.

Cooking
Work with an adult.

Banana Kabobs

Ingredients:

1 or 2 bananas

Cream Cheese or Peanut Butter

Coconut, Sprinkles, Rice Krispies,

Cocoa Krispies, Nuts (you choose)

1. Cut bananas in 2-inch pieces.
2. Roll in cream cheese or peanut butter.
3. Roll again in your choice of toppings.

Use more bananas for a large family.

No Bake Pie

Ingredients:

1 box pudding mix

1 1/2 cups milk

2 cups Cool Whip

1 graham cracker pie crust

(You choose flavors)

1. Mix pudding and milk.
2. Pour into pie crust.
3. Put in fridge for 1 hour.
4. Let Cool Whip thaw.
5. Top with Cool Whip before serving.

No Bake Cookies

Ingredients:

¼ c butter

¾ c sugar

¼ c milk

2 T cocoa

1 ¾ c oats

Optional:

¼ c peanut butter

¼ sliced almonds

1. Get an adult to help.
2. Mix butter, cocoa, sugar, and milk in 4-quart pan.
3. Boil for 1 minute.
4. Add vanilla (and peanut butter if you want it).
5. Add oats (and almonds if you want them).
6. Spread out waxed paper or plastic wrap.
7. Use a teaspoon to drop mix onto waxed paper.
8. Let cool – they will become hard.

Double the recipe if you have a large family.

Cooking

Work with an adult.

Snack Crackers

Ingredients:

1/3 cup melted butter

½ envelope ranch dressing mix

10 oz pack of oyster crackers

1. Mix butter and ranch dressing mix.
2. Put crackers in large bowl.
3. Pour butter mix over crackers.
4. Mix well.
5. Wait at least 1 hour to eat.

Ice Cream Sandwiches

Ingredients:

1 box vanilla pudding

2 cups milk

2 cups Cool Whip

1 cup mini chocolate chips

or sprinkles

24 graham crackers

1. Mix pudding and milk.
2. Put in fridge for 2 hours.
3. Add Cool Whip and chocolate chips.
4. Break graham crackers into 2 pieces.
5. Spoon pudding mix on half of crackers.
6. Top with the other half .
7. Wrap in plastic wrap
8. Freeze for 2 hours

Granola Bars

Ingredients:

2 ¼ cup oats

1 ½ cup Rice Krispies

1/3 cup melted butter

1/3 cup vegetable oil

1/3 cup honey

¾ cup packed brown sugar

1 teaspoon vanilla

½ cup mini chocolate chips

1. Grease 8x8 or 9x9 pan.
2. In large bowl, mix oats and Rice Krispies.
3. In separate bowl, mix butter and oil.
4. Add brown sugar and vanilla to butter mix.
5. Pour over oat mixture and stir.
6. Stir in chocolate chips.
7. Put in pan and cover with plastic wrap.
8. Press tightly to get out all the air.
9. Put in fridge for 2 hours.
10. Cut into bars.

There Is Something Going on Here
What comes next? Complete the pattern.

There Is Something Going on Here
What comes next? Complete the pattern.

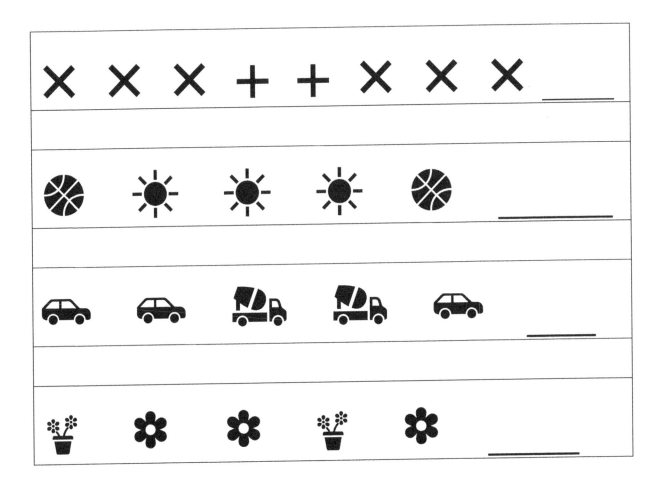

Writing Ideas

Fantasy

Write a fantasy story. Fantasy is a fiction story that could not happen in real life. Fantasy often has magical creatures that talk and is something from your imagination.

Famous Fantasies: Where the Wild Things Are, James and the Giant Peach, The Wizard of Oz.

Science Fiction

Write a science fiction story. Science fiction is fiction that is not real. It uses real science facts but is usually based on things that could happen in the future. Often includes travel to outer space.

Famous Science Fiction: Mighty Robots, Boy and Bot, Zita the Space Girl

Realistic Fiction

Write a realistic fiction story. Realistic fiction is a story that could be true, but it is not. Often a story about day to day events in the life of the main character.

Famous Realistic Fiction: Frindle, Ramona, Babysitters Club

Your Choice

Write a story about anything you are interested in. Think of the books you like to read and write about something you would read.

Connect the Dots

1. First play draws one line to connect 2 dots (up & down or across, not diagonally).
2. Next player draws one line to connect 2 dots.
3. When a box is made, the player to draw the last line, puts their initial in the box.
4. Keep going until all the dots have been connected *or you are out of time.*
5. Player with the most boxes wins the game.

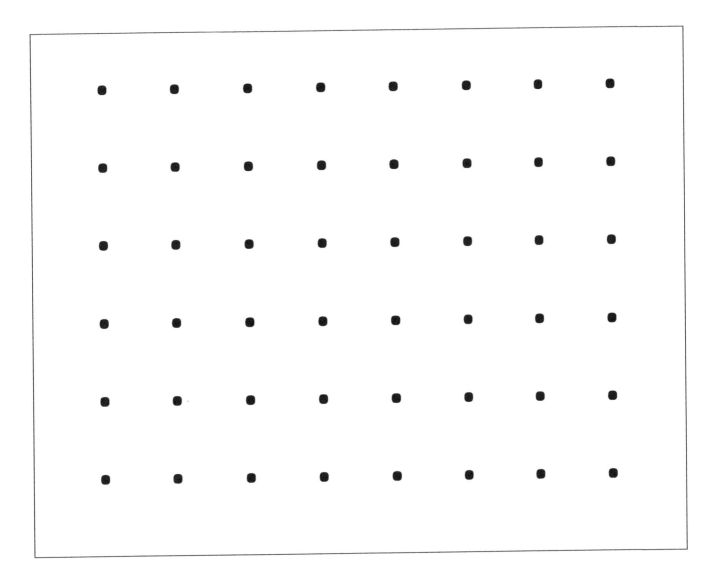

Talking with Children

There are a lot of things going on today with the outbreak of the Corona Virus. This and other things introduce a lot of change into children's lives. Some children are very laid back and just go with the flow. Others act out in response to the emotional upheaval the changes have caused. Some children internalize the confusion and worry causing parents to think the child is not experiencing stress due to the situation.

There is a lot of conflicting information in the news, causing many parents to be overwhelmed and children to be frightened. The American Academy of Pediatrics suggests that information children hear should be filtered and talked about in terms a child can understand. Here are some things you can do.

- Reassurance – Talk to children about what is being done by professionals to make people safe. Let them know that doctors and scientists are learning as much as they can about the Corona Virus. These professionals are sharing information to let us know how to stay safe.

- Anxiety – Some kids are just naturally anxious, and Corona Virus will be just one more thing to cause anxiety. Other children will be anxious because of changes that have occurred and things they are hearing. Some signs of anxiety include being clingy, being crabby, having trouble focusing, and having trouble sleeping. If your child is experiencing these symptoms, talking can help. If you don't know how to bring up a topic, read *Stuck Inside* with your child and talk about how Ben is feeling. Ask questions about Ben. Ask your child has he felt that way. Share a time you have felt that way and some things that helped such as deep breathing or exercise.

- Control – It is important for everyone to feel that they have some control over the things that are happening. Let you child know that while there are many decisions that adults make and rules that have to be followed, there are things they can to do help. Using common sense and every day hygiene are things everyone can do to help – wash hands often for 20 seconds, cough or sneeze into a tissue or their elbow, get enough sleep, and stay active. Remind your child that the body fights off germs best when it is in good shape. Don't forget to talk about avoiding people who are sick and staying home when they are sick.

- o Media – There is a lot of conflicting information on the news. No matter what channel you are watching, it is not planned with young children in mind. News has always been sensationalized to attract viewers. It is probably better if your child does not watch the news. If your child does see something frightening on TV, talk about it and what they are thinking. Talk about how the news usually has the bad stuff, but not the good things that are happening. So, it seems like it is all bad news because it is their job to tell us the bad stuff. Spend some time talking about the good things that are going on or the good side of what your child is hearing – how this information helps you to make choices that will keep you and your child safe.

- o Not Alone – Probably most important is for your child to know that he or she is not alone. Other children are worried and confused about the changes and new rules. Other children are angry and upset because they can't go see relatives of friends. Talk about how things are the same for your child and Ben. Talk about how they are different. Let your child know we are all in this together and we will all get through it together.

These are just a few points. The important thing is to talk with your child. Children are smart, they pick up on the things that are not said, the tension adults feel due to the stress, and the emotional climate change. Talking prevents children from thinking the worst and worrying about things that are never going to happen. Trauma researchers have found that children who experience trauma before they are talking have the hardest time overcoming the trauma because they can't put words to their fear. Talk with your child to build a foundation to overcome the stress whether the stress is created by a virus that is worldwide, personal health issues, or some other trauma.

Safety at Home

Wash your hands often to get rid

Of germs, including Covid.

Use a tissue or your elbow, please

When you need to cough or sneeze.

Safety in the Community

When you go out and about

Follow safety rules, without a doubt.

Stopping the spread of germs is cool.

Social distancing is the rule.

(Stay 6 feet away, when you play.)

Other Books by Angie Woodworth

Full Color Story with Activities

Available in English and Spanish

Meet the Creators

Hi, I'm Angie! I wrote this story for you and your family! I love to hike in the forest preserve when I'm not stuck inside!

Hi, I'm Lee! I drew the pictures for this story. When I'm not stuck inside I love to go to the library!

Hi, I'm Cirith! I digitally colored the pictures for *Stuck Inside*. When I'm not coloring, I'm outside rollerblading!

Made in the USA
Monee, IL
10 July 2020